WAGGON WHEELS

26 PIECES FOR VIOLA PLAYERS

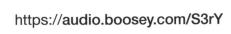

AUDIO RESOURCES

Stream or download audio for this book via the weblink below
or scan the QR code

https://audio.boosey.com/S3rY

WAGGON WHEELS | Katherine & Hugh Colledge
Copyright © 1988, 2018 by Boosey & Hawkes Music Publishers Ltd

1. In a garden

Count 4 bars

2. Summer breeze

Count 2 bars

3. Goldfish bowl

Count 2 bars

4. Penny-farthing

Count 2 bars

5. Butterflies

Count 4 bars

6. Westminster Abbey

Count 2 bars

7. Dinosaurs

Count 2 bars

8. Paddle steamer

Count 2 bars

9. Waterfall

Count 2 bars

10. Knickerbocker glory

Count 2 bars

11. Hills and dales

Count 4 bars

12. Upstairs, downstairs

Count 2 bars

13. Daydreaming

Count 2 bars

14. Bell-ringers

Count 2 bars

WAGGON WHEELS | Katherine & Hugh Colledge

15. Polka dots

Count 4 bars

16. Nightingale

Count 2 bars

17. Chinese lanterns

Count 4 bars

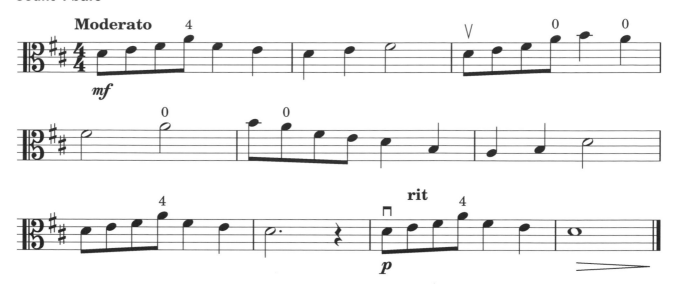

18. Fiddlesticks

Count 4 bars

19. Windscreen wipers

Count 4 bars

20. Bow ties!

Count 4 bars

21. **Ice dancers**

Count 4 bars

22. **Full moon**

Count 4 bars

23. Waggon wheels

Count 2 bars

24. With an upbeat

25. On the wing

Count 2 bars

26. Lollipop man

Count 2 bars